Father Bear's

Story by Beverley F

Illustrated by Isabel Lowe

"It's snowing," said Father Bear,
"and it's very cold.
I'm going to buy some more food.
We may be snowed in."

"I'm going to find
some more firewood,"
said Baby Bear.

On his way home with the wood, Baby Bear met Father Bear coming back from the shop.

Father Bear had a long box under one arm.
"Don't look!" said Father Bear.
"It's a surprise."

Father Bear hid the box
under his bed.

"Look at all this food,"
said Mother Bear.
"Honey and
blackberry jam;
mushrooms and
apples and fish.
We are ready
for the winter."

More snow
fell that night.
It went on snowing
for days.
The three bears
stayed asleep in bed.
They stayed asleep
for weeks!

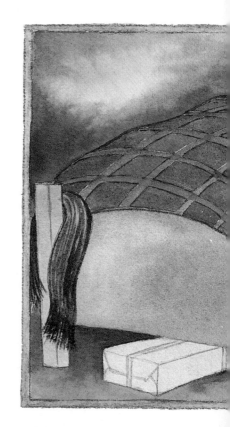

Then they all woke up.
Father Bear opened the door.
The snow came up to his nose.
"We are snowed in," he said.

"Shut the door!" said Mother Bear.
"Let's have some blackberry jam,"
she said.

"I can't play outside
with my blue car," said Baby Bear.

"No," said Father Bear. "You can't.
So it's time for my surprise.
I'm going to open my box."

"It's a **train**!" said Baby Bear.

13

"It's the toy train from the shop!" said Mother Bear.

"I love trains," said Father Bear.
"I always wanted a little train."

"Ch-ch-ch-ch," said Father Bear.

"I **like** being snowed in," said Baby Bear.